KNOCK KNOCK
and Other
SILLY JOKES

KNOCK KNOCK
and Other
SILLY JOKES

This is a Parragon book
This edition published in 2004

Parragon
Queen Street House
4 Queen Street
Bath BA1 1HE, UK

Produced by Magpie Books, an imprint of
Constable & Robinson Ltd, London

ISBN 1-40542-655-1

A copy of the British Library Cataloguing-in-Publication Data
is available from the British Library

Printed and bound in the EC

Contents

Contents Continued

Introduction

Knock Knock.
Who's there?
Sonia.
Sonia who?
Sonia shoe – and it stinks.

And there are masses more where that one came from. We've searched far and wide for rare ones, paid enormous sums of money for antique ones, snapped up a few fashionable ones and dug some up from under the bed. They're all here so get knocking and start giggling.

Knock Knock.
Who's there?
Abba.
Abba who?
Abba'out turn!
Quick march!

Knock Knock.
Who's there?
Abel.
Abel who?
Abel to see you, ha, ha!

Knock knock.
Who's there?
Ada.
Ada who?
Ada lot for breakfast.

Knock Knock.
Who's there?
Adam.
Adam who?
Adam will burst any minute now.

Knock Knock.
Who's there?
Adder.
Adder who?
Adder you get in here?

Knock Knock.
Who's there?
Ahmed.
Ahmed who?
Ahmed a big mistake coming here!

Knock Knock.
Who's there?
Aida.
Aida who?
Aida whole village cos I'm a monster.

Knock Knock.
Who's there?
Aida.
Aida who?
Aida whole box of chocolates and I feel
really sick.

Knock Knock.
Who's there?
Aileen.
Aileen who?
Aileen against my Rolls-Royce.

Knock Knock.
Who's there?
Aitch.
Aitch who?
Bless you.

Knock knock.
Who's there?
Al.
Al who?
Al be seeing you!

Knock Knock.
Who's there?
Alaska.
Alaska who?
Alaska one more time.

Knock Knock.
Who's there?
Aleta.
Aleta who?
Aleta bit of lovin'.

Knock Knock.
Who's there?
Alf.
Alf who?
Alf all if you don't catch me!

Knock Knock.
Who's there?
Alison.
Alison who?
Alison Wonderland.

Knock Knock.
Who's there?
Alma.
Alma who?
Almany times do I have to knock?

Knock Knock.
Who's there?
Althea.
Althea who?
Althea in court.

Knock knock.
Who's there?
Alvin.
Alvin who?
Alvin zis competition – just vait and see!

Knock knock.
Who's there?
Amanda.
Amanda who?
Amanda the table.

Knock knock.
Who's there?
Amber.
Amber who?
Amberter than I was yesterday.

Knock Knock.
Who's there?
Amin.
Amin who?
Amin man.

Knock Knock.
Who's there?
Ammonia.
Ammonia who?
Ammonia poor boy, nobody loves me.

Knock Knock.
Who's there?
Amos.
Amos who?
Amosquito.

Knock knock.
Who's there?
Amy.
Amy who?
Amy for the top.

Knock Knock.
Who's there?
Anais.
Anais who?
Anais cup of tea.

Knock Knock.
Who's there?
Anna.
Anna who?
Annather mosquito.

Knock knock.
Who's there?
Annabel.
Annabel who?
Annabel would be useful on this door.

Knock knock.
Who's there?
Annette.
Annette who?
Annette curtain looks good in the window.

Knock knock.
Who's there?
Annie.
Annie who?
Annie one you like.

Knock knock.
Who's there?
Anya.
Anya who?
Anya best behaviour.

Knock Knock.
Who's there?
Apple.
Apple who?
Apple the door myself.

Knock Knock.
Who's there?
April.
April who?
April will make you feel better.

Knock Knock.
Who's there?
Armageddon.
Armageddon who?
Armageddon out of here quick.

Knock Knock.
Who's there?
Army Ant.
Army Ant who?
Army Ants coming for tea then?

Knock Knock.
Who's there?
Asia.
Asia who?
Asia mum in?

Knock Knock.
Who's there?
Atomic.
Atomic who?
Atomic ache is hard to stomach.

Knock Knock.
Who's there?
Attila.
Attila who?
Attila you no lies.

Knock Knock.
Who's there?
Augusta.
Augusta who?
Augusta wind will blow the witch away.

Knock Knock.
Who's there?
Austen.
Austen who?
Austentatiously rich.

Knock knock.
Who's there?
Aurora.
Aurora who?
Aurora's just come from a big lion!

Knock knock.
Who's there?
Ava.
Ava who?
Ava good mind to leave you.

Knock Knock.
Who's there?
Avenue.
Avenue who?
Avenue learned my name yet?

Knock Knock.
Who's there?
Avis.
Avis who?
Avisibly shaken person.

Knock Knock.
Who's there?
Baby Owl.
Baby Owl who?
Baby Owl see you later, baby not.

Knock Knock.
Who's there?
Bach.
Bach who?
Bach to work.

Knock Knock.
Who's there?
Bacon.
Bacon who?
Bacon a cake in the oven.

Knock knock.
Who's there?
Barbara.
Barbara who?
(sing) "Barbara black sheep, have you any wool?"

Knock Knock and Other Silly Jokes

Knock Knock.
Who's there?
Bark.
Bark who?
Bark your car in the garage.

Knock Knock.
Who's there?
Basket.
Basket who?
Basket home, it's nearly dark.

Knock Knock.
Who's there?
Bat.
Bat who?
Bat you'll never guess!

Knock Knock.
Who's there?
Becker.
Becker who?
Becker the devil you know.

Knock Knock.
Who's there?
Bed.
Bed who?
Bed you can't guess who it is!

Knock Knock.
Who's there?
Bee.
Bee who?
Bee careful out there!

Knock Knock.
Who's there?
Beef.
Beef who?
Beef fair!

Knock Knock.
Who's there?
Belize.
Belize who?
Oh, Belize yourself then.

Knock knock.
Who's there?
Bella.
Bella who?
Bella the ball.

Knock Knock.
Who's there?
Belle.
Belle who?
Belle-t up and open the door.

Knock Knock.
Who's there?
Ben and Anna.
Ben and Anna who?
Ben and Anna split.

Knock Knock.
Who's there?
Ben Hur.
Ben Hur who?
Ben Hur an hour – let me in.

Knock Knock.
Who's there?
Benin.
Benin who?
Benin hell.

Knock Knock.
Who's there?
Berlin.
Berlin who?
Berlin maiden over.

Knock knock.
Who's there?
Bernadette.
Bernadette who?
Bernadette my dinner.

Knock Knock.
Who's there?
Bertha.
Bertha who?
Bertha day boy.

Knock knock.
Who's there?
Bethany.
Bethany who?
Bethany good shows recently?

Knock knock.
Who's there?
Bette.
Bette who?
Bette of roses.

Knock Knock.
Who's there?
Bhuto.
Bhuto who?
Bhuton the other foot.

Knock knock.
Who's there?
Bill.
Bill who?
Bill of rights.

Knock Knock.
Who's there?
Biro.
Biro who?
Biro light of the moon.

Knock Knock.
Who's there?
Bjork.
Bjork who?
Bjork in the USSR.

Knock Knock.
Who's there?
Blair.
Blair who?
Blair play.

Knock Knock.
Who's there?
Blood.
Blood who?
Blood brothers.

Knock Knock and Other Silly Jokes

Knock Knock.
Who's there?
Blue.
Blue who?
Blue away with the wind.

Knock Knock.
Who's there?
Blur.
Blur who?
Blur! It's cold out here.

Knock Knock.
Who's there?
Bolton.
Bolton who?
Bolton braces.

Knock Knock.
Who's there?
Bones.
Bones who?
Bones upon a time . . .

Knock Knock.
Who's there?
Boo.
Boo who?
Oh please don't cry!

Knock Knock.
Who's there?
Borg.
Borg who?
Borg standard.

Knock Knock.
Who's there?
Bosnia.
Bosnia who?
Bosnia bell here earlier.

Knock Knock.
Who's there?
Bowl.
Bowl who?
Bowl me over.

Knock Knock.
Who's there?
Boyzone.
Boyzone who?
Boyzone adventures.

Knock Knock.
Who's there?
Brazil.
Brazil who?
Brazil hold your breasts up.

Knock Knock.
Who's there?
Bridget.
Bridget who?
Bridget the end of the world.

Knock Knock.
Who's there?
Brighton.
Brighton who?
Brightonder the light of the full moon.

Knock Knock.
Who's there?
Briony.
Briony who?
Briony, beautiful sea.

Knock Knock.
Who's there?
Brother.
Brother who?
Brotheration! I've forgotten my own name!

Knock Knock.
Who's there?
Bug.
Bug who?
Bug Rogers.

Knock Knock.
Who's there?
Bull.
Bull who?
Bull the chain.

Knock Knock.
Who's there?
Burglar.
Burglar who?
Burglars don't knock.

Knock Knock.
Who's there?
Buster.
Buster who?
Buster blood vessel.

Knock Knock.
Who's there?
Butcher.
Butcher who?
Butcher left leg in, your left leg out . . .

Knock Knock.
Who's there?
Butter.
Butter who?
Butter wrap up – it's cold out here.

Knock Knock.
Who's there?
Caesar.
Caesar who?
Caesar arm to stop her getting away.

Knock knock.
Who's there?
Candace.
Candace who?
Candace be love?

Knock Knock.
Who's there?
Canoe.
Canoe who?
Canoe lend me some money.

Knock Knock.
Who's there?
Canon.
Canon who?
Canon open the door then.

Knock Knock.
Who's there?
Card.
Card who?
Card you see it's me!

Knock Knock.
Who's there?
Carlo.
Carlo who?
Carload of junk.

Knock Knock.
Who's there?
Carrie.
Carrie who?
Carrie on camping!

Knock Knock.
Who's there?
Cat.
Cat who?
Cat you understand?

Knock Knock.
Who's there?
Caterpillar.
Caterpillar who?
Caterpillar a few mice for you.

Knock Knock.
Who's there?
Cattle.
Cattle who?
Cattle purr if you stroke it.

Knock Knock.
Who's there?
Cecile.
Cecile who?
Cecile th-the w-windows. Th-there's a m-monster out there.

Knock Knock.
Who's there?
Cello.
Cello who?
Cello, how are you?

Knock Knock.
Who's there?
Census.
Census who?
Census presents for Christmas.

Knock Knock.
Who's there?
Cereal.
Cereal who?
Cereal pleasure to meet you.

Knock Knock.
Who's there?
Cheese.
Cheese who?
Cheese a jolly good fellow.

Knock Knock.
Who's there?
Cher.
Cher who?
Cher and share alike!

Knock Knock.
Who's there?
Chester.
Chester who?
Chester drawers.

Knock Knock.
Who's there?
Chicken.
Chicken who?
Chicken your pockets – I think your keys
are there.

Knock Knock.
Who's there?
Chile.
Chile who?
Chile without your coat on!

Knock Knock.
Who's there?
Chin and Tony.
Chin and Tony who?
Chin and Tonyk.

Knock Knock.
Who's there?
Chopin.
Chopin who?
Chopin the department store.

Knock Knock.
Who's there?
Chrysalis.
Chrysalis who?
Chrysalis the cake for you.

Knock Knock.
Who's there?
Churchill.
Churchill who?
Churchill be the best place for your
wedding.

Knock knock.
Who's there?
Clara.
Clara who?
Clara space on the table.

Knock Knock.
Who's there?
Clarence.
Clarence who?
Clarence Sale.

Knock Knock.
Who's there?
Claudette.
Claudette who?
Claudette a whole cake.

Knock Knock.
Who's there?
Clay.
Clay who?
Clay on, Sam.

Knock knock.
Who's there?
Cliff.
Cliff who?
Cliffhanger.

Knock Knock.
Who's there?
Clinton.
Clinton who?
Clinton your eye.

Knock Knock.
Who's there?
Coffin.
Coffin who?
Coffin and spluttering.

Knock Knock.
Who's there?
Cole.
Cole who?
Cole as a cucumber.

Knock Knock.
Who's there?
Colin.
Colin who?
Colin and see me next time you're passing.

Knock Knock.
Who's there?
Collie.
Collie who?
Collie Miss Molly, I don't know.

Knock Knock.
Who's there?
Congo.
Congo who?
Congo into the woods – it's dangerous.

Knock Knock.
Who's there?
Cookie.
Cookie who?
Cookien the kitchen – it's easier.

Knock Knock.
Who's there?
Corrinne.
Corrinne who?
Corrinne the bell now.

Knock Knock.
Who's there?
Cousin.
Cousin who?
Cousin stead of opening the door you're
leaving me here.

Knock Knock.
Who's there?
Cream.
Cream who?
Cream louder so the police will come.

Knock Knock.
Who's there?
Crete.
Crete who?
Crete to see you.

Knock Knock.
Who's there?
Crock and Dial.
Crock and Dial who?
Crock and Dial Dundee.

Knock Knock.
Who's there?
Cuba.
Cuba who?
Cuba wood.

Knock Knock.
Who's there?
Curry.
Curry who?
Curry me all the way.

Knock Knock.
Who's there?
Cyprus.
Cyprus who?
Cyprus the bell?

Knock Knock.
Who's there?
Czech.
Czech who?
Czech before you open the door!

Knock Knock and Other Silly Jokes

Knock Knock.
Who's there?
Daisy.
Daisy who?
Daisy that you are in, but I don't believe them.

Knock Knock.
Who's there?
Danielle.
Danielle who?
Danielle so loud, I heard you the first time.

Knock Knock.
Who's there?
Dave.
Dave who?
Dave-andalised our home.

Knock Knock.
Who's there?
De Niro.
De Niro who?
De Niro you get, the faster I run.

Knock Knock.
Who's there?
Debbie.
Debbie who?
Debbie or not to be.

Knock Knock.
Who's there?
Debussy.
Debussy who?
Debussy's never on time.

Knock Knock.
Who's there?
Delhi.
Delhi who?
Delhi a joke . . .

Knock Knock.
Who's there?
Delta.
Delta who?
Delta great hand of cards.

Knock Knock.
Who's there?
Denial.
Denial who?
Denial flows through Egypt.

Knock Knock.
Who's there?
Denmark.
Denmark who?
Denmark your own territory.

Knock Knock.
Who's there?
Depp.
Depp who?
Depp inside dear!

Knock knock.
Who's there?
Diana.
Diana who?
Diana thirst – a glass of water, please.

Knock Knock.
Who's there?
Diaz.
Diaz who?
Diaz of our lives.

Knock Knock.
Who's there?
Dickon.
Dickon who?
Dickon the right answer.

Knock Knock.
Who's there?
Diesel.
Diesel who?
Diesel make you feel better.

Knock Knock.
Who's there?
Dimaggio.
Dimaggio who?
Dimaggio yourself on a deserted island . . .

Knock Knock.
Who's there?
Disc.
Disc who?
Discusting!

Knock Knock.
Who's there?
Dish.
Dish who?
Dish ish a shtick-up!

Knock Knock.
Who's there?
Dishwasher.
Dishwasher who?
Dishwasher way I shpoke before I had my teef fixshed.

Knock Knock.
Who's there?
Dismay.
Dismay who?
Dismay surprise you but I'm from New York.

Knock Knock.
Who's there?
Distress.
Distress who?
Distress is brand new.

Knock Knock.
Who's there?
Doctor.
Doctor Who?
That's right – where's my Tardis?

Knock Knock.
Who's there?
Dolly.
Dolly who?
Dolly't us in, we're cold!

Knock Knock.
Who's there?
Donovan.
Donovan who?
Donovan the door – it's dangerous.

Knock Knock.
Who's there?
Doughnut.
Doughnut who?
Doughnut open the door whatever you do.

Knock knock.
Who's there?
Douglas.
Douglas who?
Douglas is broken.

Knock Knock.
Who's there?
Dozen.
Dozen who?
Dozen anyone know my name?

Knock Knock.
Who's there?
Drum.
Drum who?
Drum as fast as you can.

Knock Knock and Other Silly Jokes

Knock Knock.
Who's there?
Dublin.
Dublin who?
Dublin up with laughter.

Knock Knock.
Who's there?
Duke.
Duke who?
Duke come here often?

Knock Knock.
Who's there?
Duncan.
Duncan who?
Duncan make your garden grow.

Knock Knock.
Who's there?
Dutch.
Dutch who?
Dutch me in the morning.

Knock Knock.
Who's there?
Ears.
Ears who?
Ears looking at you kid.

Knock Knock.
Who's there?
Earwig.
Earwig who?
Earwigo!

Knock Knock.
Who's there?
Edna.
Edna who?
Edna cloud.

Knock Knock.
Who's there?
Egg.
Egg who?
Eggsactly.

Knock Knock.
Who's there?
Egypt.
Egypt who?
Egypt me out in the cold!

Knock Knock.
Who's there?
Eileen.
Eileen who?
Eileen against the door.

Knock Knock.
Who's there?
Eisenhower.
Eisenhower who?
Eisenhower late for work.

Knock Knock.
Who's there?
Eli.
Eli who?
Elies all the time.

Knock Knock.
Who's there?
Ellen.
Ellen who?
Ellen all the ghouls are after me.

Knock Knock.
Who's there?
Elsie.
Elsie who?
Elsie you in court!

Knock Knock.
Who's there?
Emma.
Emma who?
Emma new neighbor – come round for tea.

Knock Knock.
Who's there?
Enid.
Enid who?
Enid some shelter from the ghouls.

Knock Knock.
Who's there?
Esau.
Esau who?
Esau you in the bath!

Knock Knock.
Who's there?
Ethan.
Ethan who?
Ethan people don't go to church.

Knock Knock.
Who's there?
Euripides.
Euripides who?
Euripides, you pay for a new pair.

Knock Knock.
Who's there?
Evan.
Evan who?
Evan you should know who it is.

Knock Knock.
Who's there?
Eve.
Eve who?
Eve-ho, here we go.

Knock Knock.
Who's there?
Evie.
Evie who?
Evie weather.

Knock knock.
Who's there?
Ewan.
Ewan who?
Ewan me should get together.

Knock knock.
Who's there?
Ezra.
Ezra who?
Ezra room to rent?

Knock Knock.
Who's there?
Fang.
Fang who?
Fangs for the memory.

Knock Knock.
Who's there?
Fanta.
Fanta who?
Fanta Claus.

Knock Knock.
Who's there?
Fantasy.
Fantasy who?
Fantasy a walk in the park?

Knock Knock.
Who's there?
Fax.
Fax who?
Fax you very much.

Knock knock.
Who's there?
Felicity.
Felicity who?
Felicity getting more polluted every day.

Knock Knock.
Who's there?
Felipe.
Felipe who?
Felipe bath – I need a wash!

Knock Knock.
Who's there?
Felix.
Felix who?
Felix his bottom again I'll scream!

Knock Knock.
Who's there?
Fergie.
Fergie who?
Fergiedness sake let me in!

Knock Knock.
Who's there?
Few.
Few who?
Few! What's that smell?

Knock Knock.
Who's there?
Fido.
Fido who?
Fido known you were coming I'd have
bolted all the doors.

Knock Knock.
Who's there?
Fig.
Fig who?
Figs the step, it's broken.

Knock Knock.
Who's there?
Fish.
Fish who?
Bless you!

Knock Knock.
Who's there?
Flea.
Flea who?
Flea blind mice.

Knock Knock.
Who's there?
Florida.
Florida who?
Florida room is sticky.

Knock Knock.
Who's there?
Fonda.
Fonda who?
Fonda my family.

Knock Knock.
Who's there?
Foot.
Foot who?
Foot two pence I'd go away now.

Knock Knock.
Who's there?
Fork.
Fork who?
Forket her – she wasn't worth it.

Knock Knock.
Who's there?
Francis
Francis who?
Francis next to Germany.

Knock Knock.
Who's there?
Fred.
Fred who?
Fred I've got some bad news.

Knock Knock.
Who's there?
Freddie and Abel.
Freddie and Abel who?
Freddie and Abel to do business.

Knock Knock.
Who's there?
Fruit.
Fruit who?
Fruit of all evil.

Knock Knock.
Who's there?
Furry.
Furry who?
Furry's a jolly good fellow!

Knock knock.
Who's there?
Gail.
Gail who?
Gail of laughter.

Knock Knock.
Who's there?
Galway.
Galway who?
Galway you silly boy.

Knock Knock.
Who's there?
Gandhi.
Gandhi who?
Gandhi come out to play?

Knock Knock.
Who's there?
Gaskill.
Gaskill who?
Gaskills if it's not turned off.

Knock Knock.
Who's there?
Gazza.
Gazza who?
Gazza kiss.

Knock Knock.
Who's there?
Gerald.
Gerald who?
Gerald man from round the corner.

Knock Knock.
Who's there?
Ghent.
Ghent who?
Ghent out of town.

Knock Knock.
Who's there?
Ghoul.
Ghoul who?
Ghoulpost painter.

Knock Knock.
Who's there?
Giovanni.
Giovanni who?
Giovanniny more coffee?

Knock Knock.
Who's there?
Giuseppe.
Giuseppe who?
Giuseppe credit cards.

Knock Knock.
Who's there?
Glasgow.
Glasgow who?
Glasgow to the theater.

Knock Knock and Other Silly Jokes

Knock Knock.
Who's there?
Gopher.
Gopher who?
Gopher help – I'm stuck in the mud.

Knock Knock.
Who's there?
Gorilla.
Gorilla who?
Gorilla sausage.

Knock Knock.
Who's there?
Grace.
Grace who?
Grace your knee.

Knock Knock.
Who's there?
Grapes.
Grapes who?
Grapes Suzette.

Knock Knock.
Who's there?
Gray.
Gray who?
Grayt balls of fire!

Knock Knock.
Who's there?
Greece.
Greece who?
Greece my palm and I'll tell you.

Knock Knock.
Who's there?
Grimm.
Grimm who?
Grimm and bear it.

Knock Knock.
Who's there?
Grub.
Grub who?
Grub hold of my hand and let's go!

Knock Knock.
Who's there?
Guinea.
Guinea who?
Guinea a high five!

Knock Knock.
Who's there?
Haden.
Haden who?
Haden in the bushes.

Knock Knock.
Who's there?
Hair.
Hair who?
Hair you go!

Knock Knock.
Who's there?
Haiti.
Haiti who?
Haitit when you talk like that!

Knock knock.
Who's there?
Hannah.
Hannah who?
Hannah cloth out to dry.

Knock Knock.
Who's there?
Hand.
Hand who?
Handover your money.

Knock Knock.
Who's there?
Handel.
Handel who?
Handel with care.

Knock Knock H

Knock Knock.
Who's there?
Hardy.
Hardy who?
Hardy annual.

Knock Knock.
Who's there?
Harlow.
Harlow who?
Harlow can you get?

Knock Knock.
Who's there?
Harp.
Harp who?
Harp the Herald Angels Sing!

Knock Knock.
Who's there?
Harrison.
Harrison who?
Harrison is a credit to his father.

Knock Knock.
Who's there?
Harry.
Harry who?
Harry up! There's a ghoul after us!

Knock Knock.
Who's there?
Havana.
Havana who?
Havana spooky old time!

Knock Knock.
Who's there?
Hawaii.
Hawaii who?
Hawaii getting on?

Knock Knock.
Who's there?
Haydn.
Haydn who?
Haydn the shed.

Knock Knock.
Who's there?
Heidi.
Heidi who?
Heidi hi campers!

Knock Knock.
Who's there?
Hester.
Hester who?
Hester la vista!

Knock Knock.
Who's there?
Heywood.
Heywood who?
Heywood you open the door?

Knock Knock.
Who's there?
Hip.
Hip who?
Hippopotamous.

Knock Knock.
Who's there?
Horn.
Horn who?
Horn the way home.

Knock Knock.
Who's there?
Hosanna.
Hosanna who?
Hosanna Claus gets down our tiny chimney
I'll never know!

Knock Knock.
Who's there?
House.
House who?
Hugh's fine thanks. How's John?

Knock Knock.
Who's there?
Howl.
Howl who?
Howl I know when it's supper time?

Knock knock.
Who's there?
Huey.
Huey who?
Who am I? I'm me!

Knock knock.
Who's there?
Hugh.
Hugh who?
Hugh wouldn't believe it if I told you.

Knock Knock.
Who's there?
Ice cream.
Ice cream who?
Ice cream loudly.

Knock Knock.
Who's there?
Ida.
Ida who?
Ida thought you could say please.

Knock knock.
Who's there?
Ina Claire.
Ina Claire who?
Ina Claire day you can see forever.

Knock Knock.
Who's there?
Insect.
Insect who?
Insect your name and address here.

Knock Knock.
Who's there?
Iowa.
Iowa who?
Iowa lot to you.

Knock Knock.
Who's there?
Iran.
Iran who?
Iran all the way here. Let me in!

Knock Knock.
Who's there?
Ivana.
Ivana who?
Ivana be alone.

Knock Knock.
Who's there?
Jagger.
Jagger who?
Jaggered edge.

Knock Knock.
Who's there?
Jam.
Jam who?
Jam mind! I'm trying to think out here.

Knock knock.
Who's there?
Janet.
Janet who?
Janet a big fish?

Knock knock.
Who's there?
Jasmine.
Jasmine who?
Jasmine like to play in bands.

Knock Knock.
Who's there?
Java.
Java who?
Java cat in your house?

Knock Knock.
Who's there?
Jaws.
Jaws who?
Jaws which one you want.

Knock Knock.
Who's there?
Jeanette.
Jeanette who?
Jeanette a big fish this time?

Knock Knock.
Who's there?
Jess.
Jess who?
Jess li'l ol' me.

Knock Knock.
Who's there?
Jester.
Jester who?
Jester silly old man.

Knock Knock.
Who's there?
Jewel.
Jewel who?
Jewel know me when you open the door.

Knock Knock.
Who's there?
Jez.
Jez who?
Jezt a minute.

Knock Knock.
Who's there?
Joan.
Joan who?
Joan you know your own daughter?

Knock Knock.
Who's there?
Joanna.
Joanna who?
Joanna smack, let me in.

UNDER 5's

Knock Knock.
Who's there?
Joplin.
Joplin who?
Joplin any time you like.

Knock Knock.
Who's there?
Juan.
Juan who?
Juance upon a time there were three
bears . . .

Knock Knock.
Who's there?
Juana.
Juana who?
Juana go out with me?

Knock knock.
Who's there?
Juanita.
Juanita who?
Juanita big meal?

Knock Knock.
Who's there?
Juice.
Juice who?
Juice still want to know?

Knock Knock.
Who's there?
Juicy.
Juicy who?
Juicy what I see?

Knock Knock.
Who's there?
July.
July who?
July or do you tell the truth?

Knock Knock.
Who's there?
June.
June who?
Juneno what time it is?

Knock Knock.
Who's there?
Justine.
Justine who?
Justine the nick of time.

Knock Knock.
Who's there?
Karen.
Karen who?
Karen the can for you.

Knock Knock.
Who's there?
Keanu.
Keanu who?
Keanu let me in? It's cold out here.

Knock Knock.
Who's there?
Kent.
Kent who?
Kent see without my glasses.

Knock knock.
Who's there?
Ken.
Ken who?
Ken you come and play?

Knock Knock.
Who's there?
Kenya.
Kenya who?
Kenya guess?

Knock Knock.
Who's there?
Kermit.
Kermit who?
Kermit a crime and you go to jail.

Knock Knock.
Who's there?
Ketchup.
Ketchup who?
Ketchup the tree.

Knock Knock.
Who's there?
Kevin.
Kevin who?
Kevin it all you've got.

Knock Knock.
Who's there?
Khomeini.
Khomeini who?
Khomeini time you like.

Knock knock.
Who's there?
Kiki.
Kiki who?
Kiki's stuck in the lock – let me in.

Knock Knock.
Who's there?
Kipper.
Kipper who?
Kipper your hands to yourself.

Knock Knock.
Who's there?
Kismet.
Kismet who?
Kismet quick!

Knock Knock.
Who's there?
Knee.
Knee who?
Kneed you ask?

Knock Knock.
Who's there?
Knees.
Knees who?
Knees you every day.

Knock knock.
Who's there?
Kurt.
Kurt who?
Kurt and wounded.

Knock Knock.
Who's there?
Kylie.
Kylie who?
Kyliet your dog out for a walk?

Knock Knock.
Who's there?
Kyoto.
Kyoto who?
Kyoto the priest before the ghoulies get you.

Knock Knock.
Who's there?
Kyoto.
Kyoto who?
Kyoto town tonight!

Knock Knock.
Who's there?
Lara.
Lara who?
Lara lara laffs in Liverpool.

Knock Knock.
Who's there?
Larva.
Larva who?
Larva cup of coffee.

Knock Knock.
Who's there?
Leaf.
Leaf who?
Leaf me be!

Knock Knock.
Who's there?
Letter.
Letter who?
Letter in!

Knock Knock.
Who's there?
Lettuce.
Lettuce who?
Lettuce in and we'll tell you.

Knock knock.
Who's there?
Lily.
Lily who?
Lily livered varmint!

Knock Knock.
Who's there?
Linnekar.
Linnekar who?
Linnekars in a big traffic jam.

Knock Knock.
Who's there?
Lisa.
Lisa who?
Lisa'n life.

Knock Knock.
Who's there?
Little old lady.
Little old lady who?
I didn't know you could yodel.

Knock Knock.
Who's there?
Liz.
Liz who?
Lizen carefully, I will say this only once.

Knock Knock.
Who's there?
Lock.
Lock who?
Lock through the peephole.

Knock Knock.
Who's there?
Lolly.
Lolly who?
Lollyng about on the sofa.

Knock Knock.
Who's there?
Lulu.
Lulu who?
Lulu's not working, can I use yours?

Knock Knock.
Who's there?
Lumley.
Lumley who?
Lumley cakes!

Knock Knock.
Who's there?
Madrid.
Madrid who?
Madrid you wash my sports kit?

Knock Knock.
Who's there?
Maggot.
Maggot who?
Maggot me this new dress today.

Knock Knock.
Who's there?
Maia.
Maia who?
Maianimals are like children to me.

Knock Knock.
Who's there?
Major.
Major who?
Major answer the door didn't I?

Knock Knock.
Who's there?
Malt.
Malt who?
Maltesers the girls terribly.

Knock Knock.
Who's there?
Mamie.
Mamie who?
Mamie a new dress.

Knock Knock.
Who's there?
Manchu.
Manchu who?
Manchu your food six times.

Knock Knock.
Who's there?
Mandy.
Mandy who?
Mandy guns.

Knock Knock.
Who's there?
Mao.
Mao who?
Maothful of toffee.

Knock Knock.
Who's there?
Marcia.
Marcia who?
Marcia me!

Knock knock.
Who's there?
Maria.
Maria who?
Marial name is Mary.

Knock Knock.
Who's there?
Marie.
Marie who?
Marie me or I'll cast a spell on you.

Knock Knock.
Who's there?
Mars.
Mars who?
Marsays you've got to come home now.

Knock Knock.
Who's there?
Maude.
Maude who?
Maude of wood.

Knock Knock.
Who's there?
Mauve.
Mauve who?
Mauve over!

Knock Knock.
Who's there?
Max.
Max who?
Max Headroom.

Knock Knock.
Who's there?
Max.
Max who?
Maximum security is needed in these parts.

Knock Knock.
Who's there?
McEnroe.
McEnroe who?
McEnroe fast with his own oar.

Knock Knock.
Who's there?
Me.
Me who?
I didn't know you had a cat!

Knock Knock.
Who's there?
Mecca.
Mecca who?
Mecca my day!

Knock Knock.
Who's there?
Megan.
Megan who?
Megan a cake.

Knock Knock.
Who's there?
Melon.
Melon who?
Melond Kim.

Knock Knock.
Who's there?
Mike and Angelo.
Mike and Angelo who?
Mike and Angelo's David.

Knock Knock.
Who's there?
Mike.
Mike who?
Mike-andle's just blown out. It's all dark.

Knock Knock.
Who's there?
Minsk.
Minsk who?
Minsk meat.

Knock Knock.
Who's there?
Mint.
Mint who?
Mint to tell you earlier.

Knock Knock.
Who's there?
Missouri.
Missouri who?
Missouri me! I'm so scared!

Knock Knock.
Who's there?
Miss Piggy.
Miss Piggy who?
Miss Piggy went to market, Miss Piggy
stayed at home . . .

Knock Knock.
Who's there?
Mum.
Mum who?
Mum's the word.

Knock Knock.
Who's there?
Money.
Money who?
Money is hurting – I knocked it playing
football.

Knock Knock.
Who's there?
Monster.
Monster who?
Monster munch.

Knock Knock and Other Silly Jokes

Knock Knock.
Who's there?
Moscow.
Moscow who?
Moscow home soon.

Knock Knock.
Who's there?
Moses.
Moses who?
Moses the lawn.

Knock Knock.
Who's there?
Mosquito.
Mosquito who?
Mosquito smoking soon.

Knock Knock.
Who's there?
Moth.
Moth who?
Moth get mythelf a key.

Knock Knock.
Who's there?
Mountain.
Mountain who?
Mountain debts.

Knock Knock.
Who's there?
Muffin.
Muffin who?
Muffin to declare.

Knock Knock.
Who's there?
Munro.
Munro who?
Munro fast to the other side.

Knock Knock.
Who's there?
Murphy.
Murphy who?
Murphy, have murphy! Don't eat me!

Knock Knock.
Who's there?
Musketeer.
Musketeer who?
Musketeer a doorbell – I'm tired of
knocking.

Knock Knock.
Who's there?
Mustard.
Mustard who?
Mustard left it in the car.

Knock Knock.
Who's there?
Myth.
Myth who?
Myth Thmith thilly!

Knock Knock.
Who's there?
Nanny.
Nanny who?
Nanny people are waiting to come in.

Knock Knock.
Who's there?
Nanny.
Nanny who?
Nanny-one home?

Knock Knock.
Who's there?
Neil.
Neil who?
Neil down before the vampire king!

Knock Knock.
Who's there?
Nell.
Nell who?
Nell is hot.

Knock Knock.
Who's there?
Nestle.
Nestle who?
Nestle into the soft chair.

Knock Knock.
Who's there?
Ninja.
Ninja who?
Ninja with me every day.

Knock Knock.
Who's there?
Noah.
Noah who?
Noah counting for taste.

Knock Knock.
Who's there?
Nobody.
Nobody who?
Just nobody.

Knock Knock.
Who's there?
Noise.
Noise who?
Noise to see you.

Knock Knock.
Who's there?
Norway.
Norway who?
Norway is this your house – it's so big!

Knock Knock.
Who's there?
Nose.
Nose who?
Nosinging in the house.

Knock Knock.
Who's there?
Nougat.
Nougat who?
Nougat can go that fast!

Knock Knock.
Who's there?
Oboe.
Oboe who?
Oboe! I've got the wrong house!

Knock Knock.
Who's there?
Oil.
Oil who?
Oil be seeing you.

Knock Knock.
Who's there?
Olive.
Olive who?
Olive to regret.

Knock Knock.
Who's there?
Oliver.
Oliver who?
Oliver lone and I'm frightened of
monsters.

Knock Knock.
Who's there?
Olivier.
Olivier who?
Olivier all my money in my will.

Knock knock.
Who's there?
Onya.
Onya who?
Onya marks, get set, go.

Knock Knock.
Who's there?
Opi.
Opi who?
Opi cushion.

Knock Knock.
Who's there?
Orange.
Orange who?
Orange your day to suit the weather.

Knock Knock.
Who's there?
Organ.
Organ who?
Organize a party – it's my birthday.

Knock Knock.
Who's there?
Orson.
Orson who?
Orson, let your daddy in.

Knock Knock.
Who's there?
Owl.
Owl who?
Owl be sad if you don't let me in.

Knock Knock.
Who's there?
Oz.
Oz who?
Oz got something for you.

Knock Knock.
Who's there?
Panther.
Panther who?
Panther what you wear on your legth.

Knock Knock.
Who's there?
Paris.
Paris who?
Paris by the vampire very quietly.

Knock Knock.
Who's there?
Parsley.
Parsley who?
Parsley jam please.

Knock Knock.
Who's there?
Panon.
Panon who?
Panon my intrusion.

Knock Knock.
Who's there?
Pasta.
Pasta who?
Pasta salt please.

Knock Knock.
Who's there?
Paul and Portia
Paul and Portia who?
Paul and Portia door to open it.

Knock Knock.
Who's there?
Paul.
Paul who?
Paul your weight!

Knock Knock.
Who's there?
Pear.
Pear who?
Pear of shoes.

Knock Knock.
Who's there?
Peas.
Peas who?
Peas to meet you.

Knock Knock.
Who's there?
Pecan.
Pecan who?
Pecan boo!

Knock Knock.
Who's there?
Pen.
Pen who?
Pent-up emotions!

Knock Knock.
Who's there?
Pencil.
Pencil who?
Pencil fall down if your belt snaps.

Knock Knock.
Who's there?
Pepsi.
Pepsi who?
Pepsi through the peephole.

Knock knock.
Who's there?
Percy.
Percy who?
Percy Verence is the secret of success.

Knock knock.
Who's there?
Perry.
Perry who?
Perry well, thank you.

Knock Knock.
Who's there?
Perth.
Perth who?
Perth full of money.

Knock Knock.
Who's there?
Peru.
Peru who?
Peruse this map before you go.

Knock Knock.
Who's there?
Peter.
Peter who?
Peter cake.

Knock Knock.
Who's there?
Philippa.
Philippa who?
Philippa a bath – I'm really dirty.

Knock Knock.
Who's there?
Phone.
Phone who?
Phone I'd known it was you.

Knock Knock.
Who's there?
Piano.
Piano who?
Piano Ferries.

Knock Knock.
Who's there?
Pill.
Pill who?
Pill you open the door?

Knock Knock.
Who's there?
Pizza.
Pizza who?
Pizza this, piece of that.

Knock Knock.
Who's there?
Plums.
Plums who?
Plums me you won't tell.

Knock Knock.
Who's there?
Police.
Police who?
Police open the door.

Knock knock.
Who's there?
Poppy.
Poppy who?
Poppy'n any time you like.

Knock Knock.
Who's there?
Posie.
Posie who?
Posie hard questions.

Knock Knock.
Who's there?
Pudding.
Pudding who?
Pudding our best feet forward.

Knock Knock.
Who's there?
Puss.
Puss who?
Puss the door – it won't open.

Knock Knock.
Who's there?
Python.
Python who?
Python with your pocket money.

Knock Knock.
Who's there?
Quebec.
Quebec who?
Quebec there, if you want a ticket.

Knock Knock.
Who's there?
Queen.
Queen who?
Queen of the crop.

Knock knock.
Who's there?
Ralph.
Ralph who?
Ralph, ralph – I'm just a puppy.

Knock knock.
Who's there?
Raoul.
Raoul who?
Raoul of law.

Knock Knock.
Who's there?
Rattlesnake.
Rattlesnake who?
Rattlesnake a big difference!

Knock Knock.
Who's there?
Ray.
Ray who?
Rayning cats and dogs.

Knock knock.
Who's there?
Raymond.
Raymond who?
Raymond me to take that book back.

Knock Knock.
Who's there?
Razor.
Razor who?
Razor laugh at that joke.

Knock Knock.
Who's there?
Red.
Red who?
Red any good books lately?

Knock knock.
Who's there?
Reuben.
Reuben who?
Reuben my eyes.

Knock knock.
Who's there?
Richard.
Richard who?
Richard poor have little in common.

Knock Knock.
Who's there?
Ringo.
Ringo who?
Ringof truth.

Knock Knock.
Who's there?
Rio
Rio who?
Riorrange your appointment please.

Knock Knock.
Who's there?
Roach.
Roach who?
Roach out and touch somebody.

Knock knock.
Who's there?
Robin.
Robin who?
Robin banks.

Knock Knock.
Who's there?
Roland.
Roland who?
Roland stone gathers no moss.

Knock Knock.
Who's there?
Ron.
Ron who?
Ron answer.

Knock Knock.
Who's there?
Rosie.
Rosie who?
Rosie-lee is the best cuppa in the morning.

Knock Knock.
Who's there?
Rothschild.
Rothschild who?
Rothschild is very clever.

Knock Knock.
Who's there?
Roxie.
Roxie who?
Roxie Horror Show.

Knock Knock.
Who's there?
Royal.
Royal who?
Royal show you his paintings if you ask nicely.

Knock knock.
Who's there?
Rudi.
Rudi who?
Rudi toot!

Knock Knock.
Who's there?
Russia.
Russia who?
Russia down the shops before they close.

Knock Knock.
Who's there?
Ryder.
Ryder who?
Ryder fast horse.

Knock Knock.
Who's there?
Sacha.
Sacha who?
Sacha money in the bank.

Knock Knock.
Who's there?
Saddam.
Saddam who?
Saddam I that you couldn't come to the party.

Knock knock.
Who's there?
Sam.
Sam who?
Sam day you'll recognize my voice.

Knock Knock.
Who's there?
Scargill.
Scargill who?
Scargill not go any faster.

Knock Knock.
Who's there?
Scold.
Scold who?
Scold outside. Please let me in.

Knock Knock.
Who's there?
Scott.
Scott who?
Scott land the brave.

Knock Knock.
Who's there?
Scully.
Scully who?
Scully-wag!

Knock knock.
Who's there?
Sebastian.
Sebastian who?
Sebastian of society.

Knock Knock.
Who's there?
Serpent.
Serpent who?
Serpents are working hard, sir.

Knock Knock.
Who's there?
Seville.
Seville who?
Seville Row suit.

Knock knock.
Who's there?
Seymour.
Seymour who?
Seymour from the top window.

Knock Knock.
Who's there?
Sheik and Geisha.
Sheik and Geisha who?
Sheik and Geisha'll find.

Knock Knock.
Who's there?
Sherlock.
Sherlock who?
Sherlock your door – someone could break in.

Knock Knock.
Who's there?
Shields.
Shields who?
Shields say anything.

Knock Knock.
Who's there?
Shoes.
Shoes who?
Shoes me, I didn't mean to steal your pears.

Knock Knock.
Who's there?
Sienna.
Sienna who?
Siennathing good at the movies.

Knock Knock.
Who's there?
Sigrid.
Sigrid who?
Sigrid Service.

Knock Knock.
Who's there?
Sloane.
Sloane who?
Sloanely outside - let me in.

Knock Knock.
Who's there?
Smarties.
Smarties who?
Smartiest kid in the class.

Knock Knock.
Who's there?
Smee.
Smee who?
Smee, your friend.

Knock Knock.
Who's there?
Snow.
Snow who?
Snow business of yours.

Knock Knock.
Who's there?
Sondheim.
Sondheim who?
Sondheim soon we'll meet again.

Knock Knock and Other Silly Jokes

Knock Knock.
Who's there?
Sophia.
Sophia who?
Sophia nothing . . . fear is pointless.

Knock Knock.
Who's there?
Sorrel.
Sorrel who?
Sorrel about the mess.

Knock Knock.
Who's there?
Soup.
Soup who?
Souper Mom!

Knock Knock.
Who's there?
Spice.
Spice who?
Spice satellites are orbiting the earth.

Knock Knock.
Who's there?
Spider.
Spider who?
Spider through the keyhole.

Knock Knock.
Who's there?
Spider.
Spider who?
Spider when she thought I wasn't looking.

Knock Knock.
Who's there?
Spock.
Spock who?
Spocken like a true gentleman.

Knock Knock.
Who's there?
Stalin.
Stalin who?
Stalin for time.

Knock Knock.
Who's there?
Stan and Della.
Stan and Della who?
Stan and Dellaver.

Knock Knock.
Who's there?
Stones.
Stones who?
Stones sober.

Knock Knock.
Who's there?
Street.
Street who?
Street to go out to dinner.

Knock Knock.
Who's there?
Summer.
Summer who?
Summer good, some are bad.

Knock Knock.
Who's there?
Sweden.
Sweden who?
Sweden the pill.

Knock Knock.
Who's there?
Tango.
Tango who?
Tango faster than this you know.

Knock Knock.
Who's there?
Tarzan.
Tarzan who?
Tarzan stripes forever!

Knock Knock.
Who's there?
Teheran.
Teheran who?
Teheran very slowly – there's a monster behind you.

Knock Knock.
Who's there?
Teheran.
Teheran who?
Teheran and look me in the eye.

Knock Knock.
Who's there?
Telly.
Telly who?
Telly your friend to come out.

Knock Knock.
Who's there?
Tennis.
Tennis who?
Tennis five plus five.

Knock Knock.
Who's there?
Termite.
Termite who?
Termite's the night!

Knock Knock.
Who's there?
Thea.
Thea who?
Thea later alligator.

Knock Knock.
Who's there?
Theresa.
Theresa who?
Theresa green.

Knock Knock.
Who's there?
Thighs.
Thighs who?
Thighs the limit.

Knock Knock.
Who's there?
Thistle.
Thistle who?
Thistle be the last time I knock.

Knock Knock.
Who's there?
Throat.
Throat who?
Throat to me.

Knock Knock.
Who's there?
Thumb.
Thumb who?
Thumb like it hot.

Knock Knock.
Who's there?
Thumping.
Thumping who?
Thumping green and slimy is creeping up your leg.

Knock Knock.
Who's there?
Tic tac.
Tic tac who?
Tic tac paddy whack, give the dog a bone.

Knock Knock.
Who's there?
Tick.
Tick who?
Tick 'em up and gimme all your money.

Knock Knock.
Who's there?
Tilly.
Tilly who?
Tilly learns to say please, he'll stay outside.

Knock Knock.
Who's there?
Toffee.
Toffee who?
Toffeel loved is the best feeling in the world.

Knock Knock.
Who's there?
Too whit.
Too whit who?
Is there an owl in the house?

Knock Knock.
Who's there?
Tooth.
Tooth who?
Tooth or dare.

Knock Knock.
Who's there?
Topic.
Topic who?
Topic a wild flower is against the law.

Knock Knock.
Who's there?
Toto.
Toto who?
Totolly devoted to you.

Knock Knock.
Who's there?
Tristan.
Tristan who?
Tristan insect to really get up your nose.

Knock Knock.
Who's there?
Truffle.
Truffle who?
Truffle with you is you are so shy.

Knock Knock.
Who's there?
Tubby.
Tubby who?
Tubby or not to be.

Knock Knock.
Who's there?
Tummy.
Tummy who?
Tummy you'll always be the best.

Knock Knock.
Who's there?
Tuna.
Tuna who?
Tuna whole orchestra.

Knock Knock.
Who's there?
Turin.
Turin who?
Turin to a werewolf under a full moon.

Knock Knock.
Who's there?
Turner.
Turner who?
Turner round, there's a monster breathing
down your neck.

Knock Knock.
Who's there?
Twix.
Twix who?
Twixt you and me there's a lot of love.

Knock Knock.
Who's there?
Twyla.
Twyla who?
Twylight of your life.

Knock Knock.
Who's there?
Tyson.
Tyson who?
Tyson of this for size.

Knock Knock.
Who's there?
UB40.
UB40 who?
UB40 today – happy birthday!

Knock Knock.
Who's there?
Uganda.
Uganda who?
Uganda go away now.

Knock Knock.
Who's there?
Una.
Una who?
Yes, Una who.

Knock Knock.
Who's there?
Underwear.
Underwear who?
Underwear my baby is tonight?

Knock Knock.
Who's there?
Vault.
Vault who?
Vaultsing Matilda.

Knock Knock.
Who's there?
Venice.
Venice who?
Venice this going to end?

Knock Knock.
Who's there?
Verdi.
Verdi who?
Verdia want to go?

Knock Knock.
Who's there?
Vic.
Vic who?
Victim of a vampire.

Knock Knock.
Who's there?
Vincent.
Vincent who?
Vincent alive anymore.

Knock Knock.
Who's there?
Violin.
Violin who?
Violin horrible boy.

Knock Knock.
Who's there?
Viper.
Viper who?
Viper your nose!

Knock Knock
Who's there?
Voodoo.
Voodoo who?
Voodoo you think you are?

Knock Knock.
Who's there?
Walter.
Walter who?
Walter wall.

Knock Knock.
Who's there?
Ward.
Ward who?
Ward you want?

Knock Knock.
Who's there?
Watson.
Watson who?
Watson your head, it looks silly?

Knock Knock.
Who's there?
Webster.
Webster who?
Webster Spin, your friendly neighbourhood spider.

Knock Knock.
Who's there?
Weevil.
Weevil who?
Weevil work it out.

Knock Knock.
Who's there?
Weevil.
Weevil who?
Weevil make you talk.

Knock knock.
Who's there?
Wendy.
Wendy who?
Wendy come to take you away
I won't stop them!

Knock Knock.
Who's there?
White.
White who?
White in the middle of it.

Knock Knock.
Who's there?
Whitny.
Whitny who?
Whitnyssed the crime.

Knock Knock.
Who's there?
Wicked.
Wicked who?
Wicked make beautiful music together.

Knock Knock.
Who's there?
Wilfred.
Wilfred who?
Wilfred come if we ask nicely?

Knock Knock.
Who's there?
Witch.
Witch who?
Witch witch would you like it to be?

Knock Knock.
Who's there?
Wizard.
Wizard who?
Wizard you I'm lost.

Knock Knock.
Who's there?
Wooden shoe.
Wooden shoe who?
Wooden shoe like to know?

Knock Knock.
Who's there?
Woodworm.
Woodworm who?
Woodworm cake be enough or would you like two?

Knock Knock.
Who's there?
Worm.
Worm who?
Worm in here isn't it?

Knock Knock.
Who's there?
Yellow.
Yellow who?
Yellowver the din – I can't hear you.

Knock Knock.
Who's there?
Yoga.
Yoga who?
Yoga what it takes!

Knock Knock.
Who's there?
You.
You who?
Who's that calling out?

Knock Knock.
Who's there?
Zippy.
Zippy who?
Zippydidooda, zippydeeay!

Spooks

Why did Frankenstein squeeze his girlfriend to death?
He had a crush on her.

What did Dr Frankenstein get when he put his goldfish's brain in the body of his dog?
I don't know, but it is great at chasing submarines.

Why did Frankenstein's monster give up boxing?
He was worried he might spoil his looks.

What did Frankenstein's monster say when he was struck by lightning?
Thanks, I needed that.

What happened to Frankenstein's monster on the road?
He was stopped for speeding, fined £50 and dismantled for six months.

Dr Frankenstein: Igor, have you seen my latest invention? It's a new pill consisting of 50 per cent glue and 50 per cent aspirin.
Igor: But what's it for?
Dr Frankenstein: For monsters with splitting headaches.

What should you do if you find yourself surrounded by Dracula, Frankenstein, a zombie and a werewolf?
Hope you're at a fancy dress party.

What did one of Frankenstein's ears say to the other?
I didn't know we were living on the same block.

Igor: Only this morning Dr Frankenstein completed another amazing operation. He crossed an ostrich with a centipede.
Dracula: And what did he get?
Igor: We don't know – we haven't managed to catch it yet.

Igor: How was that science fiction movie you saw last night?
Dr Frankenstein: Oh, the same old story – boy meets girl, boy loses girl, boy builds new girl . . .

Dr Frankenstein: I've just invented something that everyone in the world will want! You know how you get a nasty ring around the bathtub every time you use it, and you have to clean the ring off?

Igor: Yes, I hate it.

Dr Frankenstein: Well you need never have a bathtub ring again! I've invented the square tub . . .

What happened when Dr Frankenstein swallowed some uranium?
He got atomic ache.

Dracula: Have you seen the new monster from Poland?

Frankenstein: A Pole?

Dracula: Yes – you can tell from his wooden expression.

Frankenstein: Help, I've got a short circuit!
Igor: Don't worry, I'll lengthen it.

Igor: Dr Frankenstein's just invented a new kind of glue.
Dracula: I hope it doesn't make him stuck up.

Monster: Someone told me Dr Frankenstein invented the safety match.
Igor: Yes, that was one of his most striking achievements.

What is written on the grave of Frankenstein's monster?
Rust in Peace.

How do you join the Dracula Fan Club?
Send your name, address and blood group.

Did you hear about Dr Frankenstein's
invention for cooking breakfast?
He crossed a chicken with an electric
organ and now he's got Hammond eggs.

What is a ghost's favourite TV program?
Horrornation Street.

When Annie first went to school she was
puzzled by people talking about the
Chamber of Horrors. "What do you mean?"
she asked nervously.
"It's what we call the staff room,"
explained her friend.

She's so scary that even spiders run away when they see her.

If a wizard were knocked out by Dracula in a fight what would he be?
Out for the Count.

Why does Dracula have no friends?
Because he's a pain in the neck.

What's Dracula's favourite dance?
The fang-dango.

What did Dracula say to the Wolfman?
You look like you're going to the dogs.

What do you get if you cross Dracula with
Al Capone?
A fangster.

Why did Dracula go to the dentist?
He had fang decay.

What does Dracula say when you tell him a new fact?
Well, fangcy that!

Why was Dracula thought of as being polite?
He always said fangs.

Did you know that Dracula wants to become a comedian?
He's looking for a crypt writer.

What do you get if you cross Dracula with Sir Lancelot?
A bite in shining armour.

What does Mrs Dracula say to Mr Dracula when he leaves for work in the evening?
Have a nice bite!

What's Dracula's car called?
A mobile blood unit.

What kind of medicine does Dracula take for a cold?
Coffin medicine.

Where is Dracula's American office?
The Vampire State Building.

What do you get if you cross a midget with Dracula?
A vampire that sucks blood from your kneecaps.

What did Dracula call his daughter?
Bloody Mary.

What is Dracula's favourite pudding?
Leeches and scream.

Two teenage boys were talking in the classroom. One said, "I took my girlfriend to see The Bride of Dracula last night."

"Oh yeah," said the other, "what was she like?"

"Well she was about six foot six, white as a ghost and she had big red staring eyes and fangs."

The other said, "Yes, but what was the Bride of Dracula like?"

Which old song did Dracula hate?
Peg O' My Heart.

Why did Dracula miss lunch?
Because he didn't fancy the stake.

What's the name of Dracula's cook?
Fangy Craddock.

Why does Dracula live in a coffin?
Because the rent is low.

When he's out driving, where does Dracula like to stop and eat?
The Happy Biter.

What is Dracula's motto?
The morgue the merrier.

What sort of ship does Count Dracula sail on?
A blood vessel.

How does Dracula keep fit?
He plays batminton.

What's Dracula's favourite society?
The Consumer's Association.

What is Count Dracula's favourite snack?
A fangfurter.

Was Dracula ever married?
No, he was a bat-chelor.

What do you think of Dracula movies?
Fangtastic!

Why is Dracula a good person to take out to dinner?
Because he eats necks to nothing.

What do you call a dog owned by Dracula?
A blood hound.

Why was Dracula always willing to help young vampires?
Because he liked to see new blood in the business.

What do yo call a ghost with no eyes?
No idea.

Patient: I keep thinking I'm a ghost.
Doctor: Well, sit down over there and let me have a look through you.

Wicked
Lessons

The school once went on an outing by train to the seaside, and the journey hadn't been progressing for very long when the teacher rushed up to the conductor and said, "Stop the train! Stop the train! One of the children has just fallen off!"

"That's all right," he replied calmly. "They'd all paid for their tickets."

The class was on a field study trip in the countryside. "What a pretty cow that is," said Annie.

"That's a Jersey," said her teacher.

"Really?" asked Annie. "I thought it was her skin."

Peter: Every Wednesday afternoon our teacher takes us out and we go for a tramp in the woods.

Anita: That sounds nice. Does the class enjoy it?

Peter: Yes, but the tramp's getting a bit fed up.

"Did you enjoy the school outing?" asked Mother.

"Oh, yes," said Jemima. "And we're going again tomorrow."

"Really?" asked Mother. "Whatever for?"

"To look for the children who got left behind."

What did the school wit say as the class boarded the boat?
Every time I go on a ferry it makes me cross.

On the train coming home Davy asked the teacher, "What was the name of that station we just stopped at?"
"I didn't notice," replied the teacher. "I was reading. Why do you ask?"
"I thought you'd like to know where Eddie and Freddie got off."

A teacher took her class for a walk in the country, and Susie found a grass snake.
"Come quickly, miss," she called, "here's a tail without a body!"

Johnny was asked if he could spell Mississippi.
He replied, "Well, I can start, but I'm not sure when to stop."

Deirdre: I wish we could go somewhere really wild and remote on our school trip.
Dora: Why?
Deirdre: I want to go where the hand of man has never set foot.

One year the school went to the Natural History Museum in London." Did you enjoy it?" asked a teacher on the way home.
"Oh yes," replied the class. "But it was a bit funny going to a dead zoo."

Mrs Broadbeam: Now, remember, children, travel is very good for you. It broadens the mind.

Sarah, muttering: If you're anything to go by, that's not all it broadens!

Naughty Nova nipped out one break time to visit the local shop.

She asked, "Have you any broken biscuits?"

"Yes," replied the shopkeeper.

"Then you shouldn't be so clumsy," said Nova cheekily.

What happened when the wizard turned a naughty schoolboy into a hare?

He's still rabbiting on about it.

Why did the wizard turn the naughty
schoolgirl into a mouse?
Because she ratted on him.

Teacher: Don't shuffle your feet when you
walk into assembly. Pick them up.
Naughty Nigel: When we've picked them
up, are we supposed to carry them in our
pockets?

Why did the teacher keep naughty Nigel in
after school?
Because she believed that detention was
better than cure.

A girl who was at a very expensive school turned up on her parents' doorstep one night, very distressed. "Daddy," she sobbed. "I's just been expelled . . ."
"Hell's Bells!" exploded her father.
"£5,000 a term and she still says 'I's'."

Why was the little bird expelled from school?
She was always playing practical yolks.

What happened to the baby chicken that misbehaved at school?
It was eggspelled.

When is an English teacher like a judge?
When she hands out long sentences.

Tracy: Would you punish someone for
something they haven't done?
Teacher: Of course not.
Tracy: Oh good, because I haven't done my
homework.

Arthur: It's true that there is a
connection between television and
violence.
Martha: What makes you think that?
Arthur: Because I told my teacher I had
watched television instead of doing my
homework, and she hit me.

Teacher: Write "I must not forget my gym kit" 100 times.
Nicky: But, sir, I only forgot it once.

Teacher: I told you to write this poem out 20 times because your handwriting is so bad.
Girl: I'm sorry, miss – my arithmetic's not that good either.

Angry Teacher: I thought I told you to stand at the end of the line!
Kevin: I did, sir, but there was someone there already!

"Boys, boys!" cried the teacher, discovering yet another scrap going on. "Didn't I tell you not to fight? You must learn to give and take!"

"That's what he did," sniffed Jerry. "He took my football and gave me a black eye!"

What do little witches like to play at school?
Bat's cradle.

What do little zombies play?
Corpses and Robbers.

"Why are you tearing up your homework notebook and scattering the pieces around the playground?" a furious teacher asked one of her pupils.

"To keep the elephants away, miss."

"There are no elephants."

"Shows how effective it is then, doesn't it?"

The schoolteacher was furious when Alec knocked him down with his new bicycle in the playground. "Don't you know how to ride that yet?" he roared.

"Oh yes!" shouted Alec over his shoulder. "It's the bell I can't work yet."

I smother school dinner with lots of honey.
I've done it all my life.
It makes the food taste funny.
But the peas stay on my knife.

The English teacher was trying to explain
what the word "collision" meant. "What
would happen," she asked, "if two boys ran
into each other in the playground?"
"They'd fight," answered the class.

What do you get if you cross old potatoes
with lumpy mince?
School dinners.

Mr Anderson, the science teacher, was very absent-minded. One day he brought a box into the classroom and said, "I've got a frog and a toad in here. When I get them out we'll look at the differences." He put his hand into the box and pulled out two sandwiches. "Oh dear!" he said. "I could have sworn I'd just had my lunch."

"I have decided to abolish all corporal punishment at this school," said the principal at morning assembly. "That means that there will be no physical punishment." "Does that mean that you're stopping school dinners as well, sir?"

Teacher: Eat up your roast beef, it's full of iron.

Dottie: No wonder it's so tough.

A warning to any young sinner:
Be you fat or perhaps even thinner,
If you do not repent,
To Hell you'll be sent,
With nothing to eat but school dinner.

Rich boy to dinner lady: This bread's horrible. Why can't you make your own bread like the servants do at home?

Dinner lady: Because we don't have the kind of dough that your father makes!

Some people say the school cook's cooking is out of this world.
Most pupils wish it were out of their stomachs.

Billy: I thought there was a choice for dinner today.
Dinner lady: There is.
Billy: No, there isn't. There's only cheese pie.
Dinner lady: You can choose to eat it or leave it.

What did the children do when there were rock cakes for lunch?
Took their pick.

What did the dinner lady say when the teacher told her off for putting her finger in his soup?
It's all right, it isn't hot.

What do Scottish toads play?
Hopscotch.

Harry: Please may I have another pear, miss?
Teacher: Another, Harry? They don't grow on trees, you know.

How can you save school dumplings from drowning?
Put them in gravy boats.

Why did Rupert eat six school dinners?
He wanted to be a big success.

"Any complaints?" asked the teacher
during school dinner.
"Yes, sir," said one bold lad, "these peas
are awfully hard, sir."
The master dipped a spoon into the peas
on the boy's plate and tasted them. "They
seem soft enough to me," he declared.
"Yes, they are now, I've been chewing them
for the last half hour."

Will and Gill were comparing school meals with their mothers' cooking. "My mum's not that good a cook," said Gill, "but at least her gravy moves about on the plate."

Paddy: Would you say the kids at your school are tough?
Maddie: Tough? Even the teachers play truant!

Wisecracks

Avril: Sometimes I really like you.
April: When's that?
Avril: When you're not yourself.

Charlie: Do you think I'm intelligent?
Chrissie: I'd like to say "yes" but my mum says I must always tell the truth.

Emma: I'd like to say something nice about you, as it's your birthday.
Gemma: Why don't you?
Emma: Because I can't think of a single thing to say!

Nellie: I have an open mind.
Kelly: Yes, there's nothing in it.

What did the builder say when he saw his non-too-bright assistant laying the lawn at a new house?
"Green on top!"

Ivan: They say Ian has a dual personality.
Ivor: Let's hope the other one is brighter than this one!

Madge: Your body's quite well organized.
Martin: How do you mean?
Madge: The weakest part – your brain – is protected by the strongest – your thick skull!

Reg: I keep talking to myself.
Roger: I'm not surprised – no one else would listen to you!

Zoe: I'm sure I'm right.
Chloe: You're as right as rain – all wet!

Jane: Do you ever do any gardening?
Wayne: Not often. Why?
Jane: You look as if you could do with some remedial weeding.

Holly: Do you ever find life boring?
Dolly: I didn't until I met you.

Why is your brother always flying off the handle?
Because he's got a screw loose.

You might find my sister a bit dull until you get to know her. When you do you'll discover she's a real bore!

His speech started at 2 p.m. sharp. And finished at 3 p.m. dull.

They call him Baby-face.
Does that mean he's got a brain to match?

They say many doctors have examined her brain – but they can't find anything in it.

Don't let your mind wander. It's not strong enough to be allowed out on its own.

Does she have something on her mind?
Only if she's got a hat on.

First explorer: There's one thing about Jenkinson.
Second explorer: What's that?
First explorer: He could go to headhunters' country without any fear – they'd have no interest in him.

Brian: Let's play a game of wits.
Diane: No, let's play something you can play too.

Jane: Do you like me?
Wayne: As girls go, you're fine. And the sooner you go the better!

Handsome Harry: Every time I walk past a girl she sighs.
Wisecracking William: With relief!

Freda: Boys whisper they love me.
Fred: Well, they wouldn't admit it out loud, would they?

Laura: Whenever I go to the local shop the shopkeeper shakes my hand.

Lionel: I expect it's to make sure you don't put it in his till.

Jerry: Is that a new perfume I smell?

Kerry: It is, and you do!

Fenton: You'll just have to give me credit.

Benton: Well, I'm certainly not giving you cash!

The problem is, his facial features don't seem to understand the importance of being part of a team.

I think she's quite old, don't you?
She's got so many wrinkles on her
forehead she has to screw on her hat.

Why do you say he's got tennis-match
eyes?
He's so cross-eyed he can watch both ends
of the court without moving his head.

She's not very fat, is she?
No, she's got a really feminine look.
Her sister's skinny, too.
Yes, if she drinks tomato juice she looks
like a thermometer.

My girlfriend loves nature.
That's very good of her, considering what nature has done to her!

Jenny: Do you like my new suit? I'm told it fits like a glove.
Lenny: Yes, it sticks out in five places.

Gorging Gordon was so large he could sit around the table all by himself.

She's so poisonous that if a dog bit her it would die.

He's so cold-blooded that if a mosquito bit him it would get pneumonia.

What's the only kind of dog you can eat?
A hot dog.

His death won't be listed under "Obituaries," it will be under "Neighbourhood Improvements."

I hear they call him Caterpillar.
Why's that?
He got where he is by crawling.

Pattie: I'd like a dress to match my eyes.
Mattie: Is it possible to buy a bloodshot dress?

I hear she's a businesswoman.
Yes, her nose is always in other people's business.

My boyfriend has only two faults –
everything he says and everything he does!

He thinks everyone worships the ground
he crawled out of.

I hear she doesn't care for a man's
company.
Not unless he owns it.

I hear he's a very careful person.
Well, he likes to economizse on soap and
water.

Doesn't he look distinguished?
He'd look better if he were extinguished.

I hear he has a quick mind.
Yes, he's a real scheme engine.

Owen: Thank you so much for lending me that money. I shall be everlastingly in your debt.
Lenny: That's what I'm afraid of!

Ronnie: I can trace my family tree way back.
Bonnie: Yes, back to the time you lived in it!

They say she has a sharp tongue.
Yes, she can slice bread with it.

Does he tell lies?
Let's just say his memory exaggerates.

Jane: I'll cook dinner. What would you like?
Shane: Good life insurance.

They say he's going places.
The sooner the better!

Harry's very good for other people's health. Whenever they see him coming they go for a long walk!

She has real polish.
Only on her shoes.

She always has an answer to every problem.
Yes, but they're always wrong.

He's watching his weight.
Yes, watching it go up!

Did you hear about the rubic cube for wallies?
It is yellow on all six sides.

What do you call a gorilla with two bananas in his ears?
Anything you like, because he can't hear you.

Ben: You'd be a great player if it weren't for two things.
Len: What are they?
Ben: Your feet.

That's Wicked

After years of traveling around the world in his search, the wicked Abanazar finally discovered the enchanted cave in which he believed lay the magic lamp which would make him millions. He stood before the boulders which sealed the cave, and uttered the magic words. "Open sesame!" There was a silence, and then a ghastly voice from within moaned, "Open says-a-who?"

Doctor: You seem to be in good health, Mrs Brown. Your pulse is as steady and regular as clockwork.
Mrs Brown: That's because you've got your hand on my watch.

That's Wicked

Did you hear about the good geography master?
He had abroad knowledge of his subject.

What is small, furry and wicked at sword fights?
A mouseketeer.

A monster went to see the doctor because he kept bumping into things. "You need glasses," said the doctor.
"Will I be able to read with them?" asked the monster.
"Yes."
"That's wicked," said the monster. I didn't know how to read before."

How do ghosts learn songs?
They read the sheet music.

At the school concert, Wee Willie had volunteered to play his bagpipes. The noise was dreadful, like a choir of cats singing off-key. After he'd blown his way through The Flowers of the Forest he said, "Is there anything you'd like me to play?" "Yes!" cried a voice from the back of the hall. "Dominoes!"

Freda: Do you like my new hairstyle?
Freddie: It's wicked. It covers most of your face.

Jimmy: Why do you always play the same piece of music at the school concert?

Timmy: Because it haunts me.

Jimmy: I'm not surprised, you murdered it weeks ago.

Soprano at concert: And what would you like me to sing next?

Member of audience: Do you know Old Man River?

Soprano: Er, yes.

Member of audience: Well go jump in it.

A gang broke into a blood bank last night and stole a thousand pints of blood. Police are still hunting for the clots.

A flute player was walking home late one night from a concert. He took a short cut through the local woods, and he hadn't gone far before he bumped into a ghost and then a vampire. Pulling out his flute he began to play a lovely trilling melody – the ghost and the vampire stood entranced. Soon a crowd of phantoms, monsters, goblins, cannibals and witches listening to the music, surrounded the musician. Then up bounded a werewolf. "Yum! Yum!" he growled, and gobbled up the flute player. "Why did you do that?" complained the others. "We were enjoying it."

"Eh, what was that?" said the deaf werewolf.

What happened when the old witch went to see a wicked movie?

The manager told her to cut the cackle.

At a concert, the boring singer with the tuneless voice announced, "I should now like to sing Over The Hills and Far Away." "Thank goodness for that," whispered someone in the audience. "I thought he was going to stay all evening."

Where do geologists go for entertainment?
To rock concerts.

Freddie had persuaded Amanda to marry him, and was formally asking her father for his permission. "Sir," he said, "I would like to have your daughter for my wife." "Why can't she get one of her own?" said Amanda's father.

A cannibal known as Ned
Ate potato crisps in his bed.
His mother said, "Sonny.
It's not very funny,
Why don't you eat people instead?"

1st monster: I have a hunch.
2nd monster: I thought you were a funny shape.

Witch: I got up really early this morning and opened the door in my nightie!
Wizard: That's a wicked place to keep a door.

Where do spiders go for fun?
To Webley.

I had a wicked dream last night, Mum.
Did you?
I dreamed I was awake, but when I woke
up I found I was asleep.

What is big, hairy and can fly faster than
sound.
King Koncord.

What did the papa ghost say to the baby
ghost?
Fasten your sheet belt.

Games mistress: Come on, Sophie. You can run faster than that.

Sophie: I can't, miss. I'm wearing run-resistant tights.

Music student: Did you really learn to play the violin in six easy lessons?

Music teacher: Yes, but the 500 that followed were pretty difficult.

I Saw a Vampire – by Ron Fast

Two fleas were running across the top of a packet of soap powder.
"Why are we running so fast?" gasped one.
"Because it says 'Tear Along the Dotted Line.'"

Why can you run faster when you've got a cold?
Because you have a racing pulse and a running nose.

A young lad was helping his dad with do-it-yourself jobs around the house. "You know, son," said the father, "you're just like lightning with that hammer."
"Fast, eh?" said the boy.
"Oh, no – you never strike in the same place twice."

Hil: Who was the fastest runner in history?
Bill: Adam. He was first in the human race.

"I hope this plane doesn't travel faster than sound," said the old lady to the flight attendant.
"Why?"
"Because my friend and I want to talk, that's why."

Dad, would you like to save some money?
I certainly would, son.
Any suggestions?
Sure. Why not buy me a bike, then I won't wear my shoes out so fast.

What's a skeleton's favourite musical instrument?
A trom-bone.

What do ghosts dance to?
Soul music.

Did you hear about the musical ghost?
He wrote haunting melodies.

Why don't skeletons play music in church?
They have no organs.

What's yellow and fills fields with music?
Popcorn.

Classified advertisement: For sale. 1926
hearse. Wicked condition; original body,

Big-headed player: I've been told I have
music in my feet.
His friend: Yes, two flats!

What happened when the umpire had a
brain transplant?
The brain rejected him.

Two hamburgers walked into a bar. The
bartender said: "Sorry, we don't serve
food."

Slimies

Worms – where's the fun in spending your entire existence burrowing through muck? Get a life!

What did one slug say to another who had hit him and rushed off?
I'll get you next slime!

How do you know your kitchen is filthy?
The slugs leave trails on the floor that read "Clean me."

What did the slug say as he slipped down the window very fast?
How slime flies!

What's the difference between school dinners and a pile of slugs?
School dinners come on a plate.

What do you do when two snails have a fight?
Leave them to slug it out.

How did the clever snail carry his home?
He used a snail-trailer.

What did the cowboy maggot say when he went into the saloon bar?
Gimme a slug of whiskey.

Why didn't the two worms go into Noah's ark in an apple?
Because everyone had to go in pairs.

What do worms leave round their bathtubs?
The scum of the earth.

How do you make a glow-worm happy?
Cut off its tail. It'll be de-lighted.

How can you tell which end of a worm is its head?
Tickle its middle and see which end smiles.

What do you get if you cross a worm with a young goat?
A dirty kid.

What do you get if you cross a glow-worm with a pint of beer?
Light ale.

Why was the glow-worm unhappy?
Because her children were not very bright.

What did the woodworm say to the chair?
It's been nice gnawing you!

What did one maggot say to the other who was stuck in an apple?
Worm your way out of that one, then!

One worm said to the other "I love you, I love you, I love you."
"Don't be stupid," the other worm said, "I'm your other end!"

Why are glow-worms good to carry in your bag?
They can lighten your load.

What is the worms' favourite band?
Mud.

What makes a glow-worm glow?
A light meal.

What's the maggot army called?
The apple corps.

What did one worm say to another when he was late home?
Why in earth are you late?

What do you get if you cross a worm with an elephant?
Big holes in your garden.

What is the best advice to give a worm?
Sleep late.

Who was wet and slippery and invaded
England?
William the Conger.

What is wet and slippery and likes Latin
American music?
A conga eel.

What do you get if you cross a snake with
a Lego set?
A boa constrictor.

What is a snake's favourite food?
Hiss fingers.

Why do babies like cobras?
Because they come with their own rattle.

Why wouldn't the snake go on the "speak-your-weight" machine?
He had his own scales.

What do you get if you cross an anaconda with a glow-worm?
A thirty-foot strip light.

What do snakes write on the bottom of
their letters?
"With love and hisses."

What did the snake say when he was
offered a piece of cheese for dinner?
"Thank you, I'll just have a slither."

What's another word for a python?
A mega-bite.

What do you get if you cross a serpent and
a trumpet?
A snake in the brass.

What is the difference between a
poisonous snake and a principal?
You can make a pet out of the snake.

Which hand would you use to grab a
poisonous snake?
Your enemy's.

What do you do if you find a black mamba
in your toilet?
Wait until he's finished.

What is a snakes favourite opera?
Wriggletto.

Why did the two boa constrictors get married?
Because they had a crush on each other.

What should you do if you find a snake in your bed?
Sleep in the wardrobe.

What snakes are good at sums?
Adders.

What do you get if you cross a snake with a hotdog?
A fangfurter.

What is a snake's favourite dance?
Snake rattle and roll.

What do you get if you cross a snake with a pig?
A boar constrictor.

What did one snake say to another?
Hiss off!

Why are snakes hard to fool?
They have no leg to pull.

What is the python's favourite pop group?
Squeeze.

What is the snakes' favorite TV program?
Monty Python.

What do you get if you cross a bag of
snakes with a cupboard of food?
Snakes and Larders.

What do you call a python with a great
bedside manner?
A snake charmer.

Why did the viper want to become a python?
He got the coiling.

What do most people do when they see a python?
They re-coil.

What school subject are snakes best at?
Hiss-tory.

What did the snake say to the cornered rat?
"Hiss is the end of the line mate!"

What do you call a snake who works for the government?
A civil serpent.

What's the best thing about deadly snakes?
They've got poisonality.

What's the snakes' favourite dance?
The mamba.

What is a snake's favourite game?
Snakes and Ladders.

What song do snakes like to sing?
Y Viva Aspaña.

What do you get if you cross two snakes
with a magic spell?
Addercadabra and abradacobra.

Why didn't the viper, viper nose?
Because the adder adder handkerchief.

What did one snake say when the other
snake asked him the time?
"Don't asp me!"

What kind of bull doesn't have horns?
A bullfrog.

What jumps up and down in front of a car?
Froglights.

When is a car like a frog?
When it's being toad.

What did the frog use to cross the road?
The green cross toad.

What did the bus conductor say to the frog?
Hop on.

What do you get if you cross a frog with a ferry?
A hoppercraft.

What do you call a frog who wants to be a cowboy?
Hoppalong Cassidy.

Why do frogs have webbed feet?
To stamp out forest fires.

What is a frog's favourite dance?
The Lindy Hop.

What do frogs sit on?
Toadstools.

What would you get if you crossed a frog
with a little dog?
A croaker spaniel.

How do frogs die?
They Kermit suicide.

Why doesn't Kermit like elephants?
They always want to play leap-frog with him.

What is a frog's favourite game?
Croak-et.

What is a frog's favourite flower?
The croakus.

What do you get if you cross a planet with
a toad?
Star warts.

A cobra was invited to dine
By his charmingly cute valentine
But when he got there
He found that the fare
Was pineapple dumplings with wine.

There was an old man called Jake
Who had a poisonous snake
It bit his head
And now he's dead
So that was the end of Jake.

A boa with coils uneven
Had the greatest trouble in breathing
With jokes she was afflicted
For her laughs got constricted
And her coils started writhing and
wreathing.

Where do you get frogs eggs?
In a spawn shop.

1st person: I've just been bitten by a
snake on one arm.
2nd person: Which one?
1st person I don't know, one snake looks
very much like the next one.

Mother: John, why did you put a slug in auntie's bed?
John: Because I couldn't find a snake.

1st man: My wife eats like a bird.
2nd man: You mean she hardly eats a thing?
1st man: No, she eats slugs and worms.

1st snake: I'm glad I'm not poisonous!
2nd snake: Why?
1st snake: Because I've just bitten my tongue.

Fisherman: What are you fishing for, sonny?

Boy: I'm not fishing, I'm drowning worms.

Boy: I once met a lion who had been bitten by a snake.

Girl: What did he say?

Boy: Nothing, silly, lions don't talk!

Surveyor: This house is a ruin. I wonder what stops it from falling down.

Owner: I think the woodworm are holding hands.

Boy: What's black and slimy, with hairy legs and eyes on stalks?
Mom: Eat the cookies and don't worry what's in the tin.

Did you hear about the stupid woodworm?
He was found in a brick.

Did you hear about the maggot that was shut up in Tutankhamun's tomb?
It had a phar-old time.

Did you hear about the woodworm who stopped doing his work?
He said it was boring.

Doctor, doctor, I think I'm turning into a frog.
Oh, you're just playing too much croquet.

Doctor, I keep thinking I'm a python.
Oh you can't get around me like that, you know.

Doctor, doctor, I keep thinking I'm an adder.
Oh good, could you help me with my tax return?

Doctor, doctor, I keep thinking I'm a toad.
Go on, hop it!

Doctor, doctor, I keep thinking I'm a snail.
Don't worry, we'll soon have you out of your shell.

Doctor, doctor, I keep thinking I'm a woodworm.
How boring.

Doctor, doctor, I keep thinking I'm a snake about to shed its skin.
Just slip into something more comfortable.

Waiter, waiter! There's a slug in my dinner.
Don't worry, sir, there's no extra charge.

Slimies

Waiter, waiter! There's a slug in my salad.
I'm sorry, sir, I didn't know you were a
vegetarian.

Waiter, waiter! There's a slug in my
lettuce.
Sorry, madam, no pets allowed here.

Waiter, waiter! There are two worms on
my plate.
Those are your sausages, sir.

John: Have you tried these paper plates?
Don: Yes, they are tearable.

Waiter, waiter! Have you got frogs' legs?
No, sir, I always walk like this.

Waiter, waiter, are there snails on the menu?
Oh yes, sir, they must have escaped from the kitchen.

Waiter, waiter! I can't eat this meat, it's crawling with maggots.
Quick, run to the other end of the table, you can catch it as it goes by.

Waiter, waiter! There's a slug in my lettuce.
Quiet, they'll all want one.

Waiter, waiter! There's a frog in my soup.
Don't worry, madam, there's not enough there to drown him.

A snake went into a café and ordered a cup of tea. "That will be $2," said the waitress, "and may I say that it's nice to see you here. We don't get many snakes coming in here." "I'm not surprised at $2 for a cup of tea!" he replied.

Spook: Should you eat spiders and slugs and zombie slime on an empty stomach?
Witch: No, you should eat them on a plate.

What is a snail?
A slug with a crash helmet.

What did the witch say to the ugly toad?
"I'd put a curse on you – but somebody beat me to it!"

A woman walked into a pet shop and said, "I'd like a frog for my son."
"Sorry madam," said the shopkeeper, "we don't do part exchange."

A frog walked into a library and asked the librarian what he would recommend. "How about this, sir?" asked the librarian, showing him Toad of Toad Hall. "Reddit, reddit," said the frog.

Did you hear about the snake with a bad cold?
No! Tell me about the snake with a bad cold.
It had to viper nose.

Did you hear about the scientist who crossed a parrot with a crocodile?
It bit off his arm and said, "Who's a pretty boy then?"

What's a crocodile's favourite game?
Swallow my leader.

Dad, do slugs taste nice?
Of course not, why do you ask?
Because you've just eaten one that was in your salad.

A snail was mugged in an alley by two slugs. Later a detective asked him for a description of his assailants. "Gee," said the snail, "I am not sure. It all happened so fast."

Guys and Gals

What do you call an insect from outer space?
Bug Rogers.

What do you get if you cross the Lone Ranger with an insect?
The Masked-quito.

What powerful reptile is found in the Sydney Opera House?
The Lizard of Oz.

What is Dr Jekyll's favourite game?
Hyde and Seek.

What do you get if you cross a toad with a mist?
Kermit the Fog.

Who has large antlers, has a high voice and wears white gloves?
Mickey Moose.

Did you know that Dr Jekyll has created a new medicine?
One sip and you're a new man.

Which candles burn longer, red or blue?
Neither, they both burn shorter.

Why did the witch keep turning people into Mickey Mouse?
She was having Disney spells.

What's the quickest way to Dracula's heart?
Through his chest.

What is the vampire's favourite breakfast cereal?
Ready Neck.

What's a vampire's favourite cartoon character?
Batman.

What is green and sooty and whistles when it rubs its back legs together?
Chimney Cricket.

What do you get if you cross a flea with a rabbit?
A bug's bunny.

Two fleas were sitting on Robinson Crusoe's back. One hopped off saying, "Byee! See you on Friday!"

What do Paddington Bear and Winnie the Pooh pack for their holidays?
The bear essentials.

What's large and green and sits in a corner on its own all day?
The Incredible Sulk.

Why was Baron Frankenstein never lonely?
Because he was good at making fiends.

Little Miss Muffet sat on a tuffet
Eating a bowl of stew
Along came a spider
And sat down beside her.
Guess what?
She ate him up too!

What do you get if a huge hairy monster
steps on Batman and Robin?
Flatman and Ribbon.

What did ET's mother say to him when he
got home?
Where on Earth have you been?

Why does the Hound of the Baskervilles turn around and around before he lies down for the night?
Because he's the watchdog and he has to wind himself up.

Did you hear about the monster who was known as Captain Kirk?
He had a left ear, a right ear and a final front ear.

Why did J.R. see his lawyer?
Because he wanted to Sue Ellen.

What does Rudolph the Red-Nosed
Reindeer say before he tells a joke?
"This one will sleigh you!"

The wonderful Wizard of Oz
Retired from business becoz
What with up-to-date science
To most of his clients
He wasn't the wiz that he woz.

Which ghost sailed the seven seas looking
for garbage and blubber?
The ghost of BinBag the Whaler.

Superman climbed to the top of a high mountain in the middle of the African jungle. As he reached the summit he found himself suddenly surrounded by dozens of vicious vampires, ghosts, monsters and goblins. What did he say?

"Boy, am I in the wrong joke!"

Who carries a sack and bites people?
Santa Jaws.

Who is Wyatt Burp?
The sheriff with the repeater.

If King Kong went to Hong Kong to play ping-pong and died, what would they put on his coffin?
A lid.

Where does Tarzan buy his clothes?
At a jungle sale.

What lives in a pod and is a Kung Fu expert?
Bruce Pea.

What's big, hairy and can fly?
King Koncorde.

What illness did everyone on the
Enterprise catch?
Chicken Spocks.

What does Luke Skywalker shave with?
A laser blade.

Who is in cowboy movies and is always
broke?
Skint Eastwood.

Why did Mickey Mouse take a trip to outer
space?
He wanted to find Pluto.

How did Benjamin Franklin discover electricity?
It came to him in a flash.

What's the difference between Noah's Ark and Joan of Arc?
One was made of wood and the other was Maid of Orleans.

Who conquered half the world, laying eggs along the way?
Attila the Hen.

Why was Cleopatra so cantankerous?
She was Queen of Denial.

"Who's been eating my porridge?"
squeaked Baby Bear.

"Who's been eating my porridge?" cried
Mother Bear.

"Burp!" said Father Bear.

Why wouldn't the ripe peach sit on the
wall?

It had heard what happened to Humpty
Dumpty.

Fan: I've always admired you. Are your
teeth your own?

Actor: Whose do you think they are?

Did you hear about the film star who had so many facelifts that when she went for the next one they had to lower her body instead?

What was purple and ruled the world?
Alexander the Grape.

Which was the smallest plum?
Tom Plum.

Who was the first underwater spy?
James Pond.

Who marched 10,000 pigs up a hill and
back down again?
The Grand Old Duke of Pork.

What happened to the pig who studied
Shakespeare?
He ended up in Hamlet.

What was Noah's job?
Preserving pears.

What do you call a donkey with three legs?
A wonkey.

How do Daleks deal with eggs?
They eggs-terminate them.

Jane: I can trace my heritage all the way
back to royalty.
Jill: King Kong?

What were Tarzan's last words?
"Who greased that vine?"

What was King Arthur's favourite game?
Knights and crosses.

Why did King Henry VIII have so many wives?
He liked to chop and change.

What do you call a top pop group made up of nits?
The Lice Girls.

What's the grasshoppers' favorite band?
Buddy Holly and the Crickets.

What is the insects' favourite pop group?
The Beatles.

Which ghost was President of France?
Charles de Ghoul.

Who is the worms' Prime Minister?
Maggot Thatcher.

Which skeleton wore a kilt?
Boney Prince Charlie.

What do you call the famous eighteenth-century skeleton who was cremated?
Bone-ash (Beau Nash . . . geddit?)

Wizard: You have the face of a saint.
Witch: Really? Which one?
Wizard: A Saint Bernard.

Teacher: What did Robert the Bruce do after watching the spider climbing up and down?
Pupil: He went and invented the yo-yo.

Who is the most royal ant?
Princess Ant.

Who was the most famous French ant?
Napoleant.

A man came home from work one day to find a ghostly figure with lots of wild hair, a long, ragged jacket and big staring eyes.
"Who are you?" asked the man.
"I am the ghost of Beethoven," said the apparition.
"I don't believe you," said the man. "If you are Beethoven, perform his last movement."
"All right," said the ghost and fell off the piano stool.

Who was the most famous scientist ant?
Albert Antstein.

Two friends were discussing the latest scandalous revelations about a Hollywood actress. "They say she likes her latest husband so much she's decided to keep him for another month," said one to the other.

Doctor, doctor, I think I'm Napoleon.
How long have you felt like this?
Ever since Waterloo.

Nicky and Vicky were talking about a famous, very glamorous movie star. "What do you think of her clothes?" asked Nicky. "I'd say they were chosen to bring out the bust in her," replied Vicky.

What did the cannibal say when he met the famous explorer?
Dr Livingstone, I consume?

What did Hannibal say when he saw the elephants coming?
"Here come the gooseberries" – he was color-blind.

What's yellow and sings?
Banana Mouskouri.

What's short and green and goes camping?
A boy sprout.

How did they divide the Roman Empire?
With a pair of Caesars.

Who wrote Great Eggspectations?
Charles Chickens.

What do you get if you cross a pop singer
with a shark?
Boy Jaws.

A fan approached a famous tennis player.
"May I have your autograph, please?" she
asked. The tennis player was in a hurry, so
he said, "I don't really play tennis, you
know." "I know," said the fan. "But I'd like
your autograph anyway."

Has success gone to his head?
"I don't know, but it's certainly gone to his
mouth!"

Witches

1st witch: Why aren't we getting any sun then?
2nd witch: Because she can't spell "sunny."

What did one witch say to the other when they came out of the cinema?
"Do you want to walk home or shall we take the broom?"

What's a witch's favourite book?
Broom at the Top.

What's the witches' favourite pop group?
Broomski Beat.

Why did the witch join Tottenham
Hotspur Football Club?
She heard they needed a new sweeper.

What makes more noise than an angry
witch?
Two angry witches.

What do little witches like to play at
school?
Bat's cradle.

What happened to the witch with an
upside-down nose?
Every time she sneezed her hat blew off.

What happened when the baby witch was born?
It was so ugly its parents ran away from home.

What happened when the witch went for a job as a TV presenter?
The producer said she had the perfect face for radio.

What kind of music do witches play on the piano?
Hag-time.

What is old and ugly and can see just as well from both ends?
A witch with a blindfold.

What do witches eat for breakfast?
Rice Krispies because they snap at them.

What do witches eat for dinner?
Real toad in the hole.

What is the best way of stopping infection from witch bites?
Don't bite any witches.

What should you expect if you drop in on a witch's home unexpectedly?
Pot luck.

What does a witch do if her broom is stolen?
She calls the Flying Squad.

What do you call a witch who climbs up walls?
Ivy.

Where do the cleanest witches live?
Bath.

Witches

What do you call a witch with one leg?
Eileen.

How can you tell if a witch has a glass eye?
When it comes out in conversation.

What goes "cackle, cackle, bonk?"
A witch laughing her head off.

What is the witch's motto?
We came, we saw, we conjured.

How can you make a witch itch?
Take away her "W."

How does a witch tell the time?
With her witch watch.

What are little witches good at in school?
Spelling.

How does a witch-doctor ask a girl to polka
with him?
Voodoo like to dance with me?

What do you call a nervous witch?
A twitch.

Who's the fastest witch?
The one that rides on a vrooooooom stick.

Why do witches fly on broomsticks?
Because vacuum cleaners are too heavy.

What do you get if you cross a sorceress
with a millionaire?
A very witch person.

What kind of tests do they give in witch
school?
Hex-aminations.

How do witches on broomsticks drink their tea?
Out of flying saucers.

Where does a witch keep her purse?
In a hag bag.

What do witches ring for in a hotel?
B-room service.

What kind of jewellry do warty witches wear on their wrists?
Charm bracelets.

What happens if you are confronted with two identical hags?
You can't tell witch is witch.

How do you know that you're in bed with a witch?
She has a big "W" embroidered on her pajamas.

When should you feed witch's milk to a baby?
When it's a baby witch.

What is a little witch after she is one year old?
A two-year-old witch.

What do you call a witch who drives really badly?
A road hag.

What is another term for a witch?
A hag lady.

What do you call a witch who is made of cotton and has lots of holes in her?
A string hag.

Why should men be careful of beautiful witches?
They'll sweep them off their feet.

Is it true that a witch won't hurt you if you run away from her?
It all depends on how fast you run!

What do you call a witch who kills her mother and father?
An orphan.

Why do some witches eat raw meat?
Because they don't know how to cook.

How do you make a witch float?
Take two scoops of ice cream, a glass of
Coke and one witch.

What type of boats do witches sail?
Cat-amarans.

What's yellow and very poisonous?
Witch-infested custard.

Why did the witch buy two tickets to the zoo?
One to get in and one to get out.

What do baby witches play with?
Deady bears.

How can you tell when witches are carrying a time bomb?
You can hear their brooms tick!

How do warty witches keep their hair out of place?
With scare spray.

Why is "s" the witches' favorite letter?
Because it turns cream into scream.

What do you call a pretty and friendly witch?
A failure.

Why are witches' fingernails never more than eleven inches long?
Because if they were twelve inches they'd be a foot.

What do you call a witch who flies in Concorde?
Lucky.

What is evil and ugly, puts spells on people
and is made of leaves?
A witch (the leaves were just a plant).

What do you do with a blue witch?
Try to cheer her up.

What does a witch turn into when the
lights go out?
The dark.

Why do witches go to the docks?
To see the bats being launched.

What do you do if a witch in a pointy hat sits in front of you in a movie theater?
Miss most of the movie.

How is a witch's face like a million dollars?
It's all green and wrinkly.

What's evil and ugly and goes up and down all day?
A witch in an elevator.

Why did the witches go on strike?
Because they wanted sweeping reforms.

What do you call a which who likes the beach but is scared of the water?
A chicken sand-witch.

Who went into a witch's den and came out alive?
The witch.

What do you call two witches who share a broomstick?
Broom-mates.

What do witches use pencil sharpeners for?
To keep their hats pointed.

What is evil, ugly and keeps the neighbours awake?
A witch with a drumkit.

Why do witches have stiff joints?
They get broomatism.

Why did the witch ride on a French duster?
She felt like a dust-up.

Are you getting sick of witch jokes?
Then cancel your subscription to witch.

When a witch falls into a pond what is the first thing that she does?
Gets wet.

There once was a man name of Crocket
Who stuck his foot in a socket.
Then along came a witch
Who turned on the switch
And Crocket went up like a rocket!

What's black and goes round and round?
A witch stuck in a revolving door.

What would you say if you saw nine witches in black capes flying south and one witch in a red cape flying north?
That nine out of ten witches wear black capes.

What do you call it when a witch's cat falls off her broomstick?
A catastrophe.

What do you get if you cross a witch's cat with Father Christmas?
Santa Claws.

How do you get milk from a witch's cat?
Steal her saucer.

What do witches' cats like for breakfast?
Mice Krispies.

What do you get if you cross a witch's cat
with a canary?
A peeping tom.

What did the witch give her lazy cat?
Mouse-flavoured cat food.

Why did the witch feed her cat with dimes?
She wanted to put them in the kitty.

Witch: How can I lose some of this ugly fat?
Doctor: Cut your head off.

There was a young witch from Tintyre
Whose voice went up higher and higher,
Till one Sunday night
It vanished from sight
And turned up next day in the fire.

What does a witch enjoy cooking most?
Gnomelettes.

Why is a witch's kitten like an unhealed wound?
Both are a little pussy.

What do you call a witch's cat that drinks vinegar?
A sour puss.

What do you call a witch's cat who never comes when she's called?
Im-puss-able.

What has four legs, a tail, whiskers and flies?
A dead witch's cat.

What do you get if you cross a witch's cat and a canary?
A cat with a full tummy.

1st boy: Are you having a party for your birthday?
2nd boy: No, I'm having a witch do.
1st boy: What's a witch do?
2nd boy: She flies around on a broomstick casting spells.

1st witch: I spend hours in front of the mirror admiring my beauty. Do you think that's vanity?
2nd witch: No, it's imagination.

Witch: I have the face of a 16-year-old girl.
Wizard: Well you'd better give it back, you're making it all wrinkly.

1st witch: What's your new boyfriend like?
2nd witch: He's mean, nasty, ugly, smelly, and totally evil – but he has some bad points too.

1st witch: I went to the beauty parlor yesterday. I was there for three hours.
2nd witch: Oh, what did you have done?
1st witch: Nothing, I was just going in for an estimate.

1st witch: I'm going to France tomorrow.
2nd witch: Are you going by broom?
1st witch: No, by hoovercraft.

Witch: You should keep control of your little boy. He just bit me on the ankle.
Vampire: That's only because he couldn't reach your neck.

Wild
Animals

What's the difference between a very old, shaggy yeti and a dead bee?
One's a seedy beast and the other's a deceased bee.

What do you get if you cross an octopus with a skunk?
An octopong.

What do you get if you cross a giant, hairy monster with a penguin?
I don't know but it's a very tight-fitting dinner suit.

Why do polar bears like bald men?
Because they have a great, white, bear place.

What kind of money do yetis use?
Iced lolly.

What exams do yetis take?
Snow levels.

What do you get if you cross a bee with a skunk?
A creature that stinks and stings.

What happened to the cannibal lion?
He had to swallow his pride.

What was the name of the film about a
killer lion that swam underwater?
"Claws."

Why don't anteaters get sick?
Because they're full of anty-bodies!

What do you get it you cross a hedgehog
with a giraffe?
A long-necked toothbrush.

What's a porcupine's favourite food?
Prickled onions.

What's black and white and makes a lot of noise?
A zebra with a set of drums.

What should you do if you find a gorilla sitting at your school desk?
Sit somewhere else.

What did the stupid ghost call his pet tiger?
Spot.

Why was the mother kangaroo cross with her children?
Because they ate crisps in bed.

What's the difference between a coyote and a flea?
One howls on the prairie, and the other prowls on the hairy.

Have you ever seen a man-eating tiger?
No, but in the café next door I once saw a man eating chicken!

A group of Chinese who were on safari in Africa came across a pride of lions. "Oh look," said one of the lions. "A Chinese takeaway."

1st lion: Every time I eat, I feel sick.
2nd lion: I know. It's hard to keep a good man down.

What's green and wobbly and hangs from trees?
Giraffe snot.

The eighth Earl of Jerry was showing
Americans round his ancestral home, Jerry
Hall, when one of them pointed to a moth-
eaten, stuffed polar bear. "Gee! That
beast sure smells," said the American.
"Why d'ya keep it?"
"For sentimental reasons. It was shot by
my mother when she and my father were
on a trip to the Arctic."
"What's it stuffed with?" asked the
American.
"The seventh Earl of Jerry!"

What's the difference between a
gooseberry, a gorilla, and a tube of glue?
I don't know.
Well, you can bite into a gooseberry, but
you can't bite into a gorilla.

What about the tube of glue?
I thought that was where you'd get stuck!

What's an alligator's favourite game?
Snap.

Why shouldn't you play cards in the jungle?
There are too many cheetahs.

What do you get if you cross an OXO cube
with a hyena?
A laughing stock.

What do you get if you cross a giraffe
with a hedgehog?
A hairbrush with a very long handle.

Why did King Kong want to join the army?
Because he wanted to study gorilla
warfare.

We had roast boar for dinner last night.
Was it a wild boar?
Well, it wasn't very pleased.

Teacher: Now, today, we're going to study the wildlife of Africa, starting with elephants. Now pay attention and look at me or you may never know what an elephant looks like!

Where do you find wild yetis?
It depends where you left them.

What's the difference between a wild camel and a bully?
One's a big, smelly, bad-tempered beast and the other is an animal.

What do you get if you cross a dog with a lion?
A terrified mailman.

The great Roman emperor Caesar was watching Christians being thrown to the lions. "One good thing about this sport," he said to one of his aides, "we're never bothered with spectators running onto the pitch."

A question in Sam's biology exam asked him to name ten animals that were found in Africa. Sam wrote down, "Nine elephants and a lion."

Did you hear about the boy who was told to do 100 lines?
He drew 100 cats on the paper. He thought the teacher had said lions.

In the park this morning I was surrounded by lions.
Lions! In the park?
Yes – dandelions!

Dad was taking Danny around the museum when they came across a magnificent stuffed lion in a glass case. "Dad," asked the puzzled Danny, "how did they shoot the lion without breaking the glass?"

On which side does the tiger have most of his stripes?
On the outside.

What's worse than a giraffe with a sore throat?
A centipede with chilblains.

Some vampires went to see Dracula.
They said, "Drac, we want to open a zoo.
Have you got any advice?"
"Yes," replied Dracula, "have lots of
giraffes."

What did the cowboy say when the bear
ate Lassie?
Well, doggone!

What animal do you look like when you get
into the bath?
A little bear.

Why shouldn't you take a bear to the zoo?
Because they'd rather go to the movies.

What should you call a bald teddy?
Fred bear.

What's got two humps and changes colour?
A camel-ion.

What is a bear's favourite drink?
Koka-Koala.

What do you get if you cross a skunk with a bear?
Winnie the Pooh.

Have you ever hunted bear?
No, but I've been shooting in my shorts.

What do you get if you cross a teddy bear with a pig?
A teddy boar.

Why do bears have fur coats?
Because they'd look stupid in anoraks.

What's a teddy bear's favourite pasta?
Tagliateddy.

How do you hire a teddy bear?
Put him on stilts.

Why was the little bear so spoiled?
Because its mother panda'd to its every
whim.

Teddy: If you were walking through a
Canadian forest and you met a bear, would
you keep on walking or turn round and run?
Eddie: I'd turn round and run.
Teddy: What, with a bear behind?

Why do bears wear fur coats?
They'd look silly in plastic macs.

How do you start a teddy bear race?
Say, "Ready, teddy, go!"

What's a stone's favourite music?
Rock and Roll.

The
End